The Fifth Question

Sandy Anderson

Trilogy Christian Publishers
A Wholly Owned Subsidary of Trinity Broadcasting Network
2442 Michelle Drive
Tustin, CA 92780

Cover design by: Cornerstone Creative Solutions

For information, address Trilogy Christian Publishing
Rights Department, 2442 Michelle Drive, Tustin, Ca 92780.
Trilogy Christian Publishing/ TBN and colophon are trademarks of Trinity Broadcasting Network.

For information about special discounts for bulk purchases, please contact Trilogy Christian Publishing.

Manufactured in the United States of America

10 9 8 7 6 5 4 3 2 1

Library of Congress Cataloging-in-Publication Data is available.

ISBN 978-1-63769-448-0 (Print Book)
ISBN 978-1-63769-449-7 (ebook)

For Jayne, with my apology for letting you down. I still have your letter. May you find your Messiah and experience His love and peace. I hope to see you in heaven someday.

Acknowledgments

Thanks for all the input and encouragement from my writers group: Barb, Jan, Mary, Joni, and Pat. Special thanks to Joyce for the Hebrew lessons and to Lisa for reminding me that this is a children's book. That helped me find the right answer to the fifth question. Thank you, Pam and Tom, for the technical help. Thanks also to my son Jim and his wife, Laurie; son Tom; and grandsons Blake and John for your years of love and support. And last, but not least, thank You, Jesus the Messiah, for Your love and forgiveness and for eternal life.

He knew he was in trouble again when he heard his full name.

"Daniel Alan Beckman!" his mother warned. "If you ask me one more question, I'm going to scream!"

Danny couldn't help it. He just had to know things. Why does the sun come up in the east? Does it come up in the east every day or just on Monday, Wednesday, and Friday? Where does the sun go when it's dark outside?

Danny's dad would usually answer three or four questions before he got tired of it. Danny's mom heard his questions all day long, and sometimes, she put her fingers in her ears and ran out of the room.

Danny's teacher tried not to look at him when he raised his hand. She knew he would ask a hard question. And another. And another.

Even Danny's new best friend, Joey, got upset with him. "Why do you always answer my questions with a question?" he asked, frowning.

"Why not?" asked Danny.

The only time Danny could ask question after question without getting into trouble was at Passover. Since he was the youngest child in the family, Danny got to ask the four questions at the Seder, the special Passover meal.

Last year, Danny's dad had hurried right on with the answers from the Haggadah, the Passover book. Danny still remembered the question he had wanted to ask. "This year, I'll get an answer!" he promised himself.

"I need your help, Danny," his mom told him. "This house has to be cleaned from top to bottom before Passover."

Danny and his mom threw out all the bread and other food that had yeast. They got out the special dishes and polished the silverware until it sparkled.

"Hey, Mom, is it time to set the table now?" Danny asked. Just before the company came for the Seder, he put a plate, a napkin, a cup, and silverware at each place. His mom put a Haggadah next to each plate and a pillow on each chair.

Danny's dad answered the door and welcomed Aunt Esther and Uncle Sammy. Danny grinned at his cousins, Marc and Gaby. Everyone gathered around the table. The children quietly looked at the candles and the Seder plate with the five kinds of food on it. They looked at the plate of three matzahs covered with a special cloth, the dish of salt water, and the bottle of grape juice. They silently pointed to the extra cup on the table.

Danny's mom lit the candles to begin the Seder. Danny tried to pay attention as the blessings were asked. He ate a piece of parsley dipped in salt water. He and Marc and Gaby pretended not to see his dad break the middle matzah, wrap the biggest piece, the Afikomen, in a napkin, and leave the table to hide it.

His dad started the story of Passover, and soon, it was Danny's turn to speak and to use his favorite word. "*Why* is this night different from all other nights?"

1. Why can we only eat matzah tonight?
2. Why can we only eat a bitter vegetable tonight?
3. Why do we have to dip the foods twice tonight?
4. Why do we have to lean on pillows tonight?

Danny's dad quickly began to answer the four questions.

"But, Dad," Danny interrupted, "I have another question."

"Not now, Danny," said his dad. "Later. Okay?" He looked at the people around the table. "At least we know that he's the wise child of the Haggadah," he said, laughing. "He asks lots of questions!"

Danny stopped talking, but he didn't stop thinking. His dad was telling the story of that time in Egypt years ago when the Israelites were slaves.

Danny stopped listening and started daydreaming. He imagined that he was living back then in Egypt. He saw his dad come home tired and dirty from making bricks. His mom cried salty tears. His dad whispered to his mom, "They say this man Moses will make Pharaoh let us go free. God promised it before we were born."

That night in Egypt, Danny watched his dad use branches to put the blood of a lamb on the doorpost of their house. "Dad! Why are you doing that?" Danny asked.

"You've heard about all the strange things that have been happening, Danny," his dad said. "You know about the frogs, the flies, the hail, and other things that have happened to the Egyptians because Pharaoh won't let us leave Egypt. Now Moses has told us to do this so God will pass over our house and you will be safe."

In the morning, Danny heard the screaming from the Egyptians who did not put the blood on their houses. Then excited voices called out. "We're leaving! God answered our prayers! Everyone get ready quickly!" Danny's mom hurried to gather their clothes and the bread dough that wasn't yet ready to bake.

"Where are we going?" Danny asked her. "And when are we going to eat?"

"They say we are going to a better land, Danny," she said. "It's a place where there is good food and where we won't have to work so hard. We'll be free there. Hurry now. We're leaving right away. When we stop to rest, I'll bake this dough into flatbread."

"But, Mom," Danny said, "why…?"

"No questions now, Danny," his mom impatiently said. "Just get ready."

A little while later, Danny and his mom and dad began walking with the other Israelites. Everyone carried big bundles. People were laughing and crying. Mothers were trying to keep track of their children. Danny turned to ask his mom a question. "Mom?"

Oh no! He couldn't see her anywhere. All he could see were legs and stomachs. He was pushed around by the crowd. A big hand grabbed his shoulder.

"Danny, don't wander around. Stay close to your mother."

Danny had never been so glad to hear his dad's voice. His dad steered him to his mother's side. Danny's legs were already tired from walking. "Mom," he whined, "when are we going to be there?"

"I don't know, Danny," she said. "Keep walking and don't ask questions."

"We've walked about a million miles!" Danny said to himself. He couldn't see where they were going because of all the people, but he could see a big white cloud moving in front of them. That night, the cloud turned into fire and led the way.

"The fire part is pretty cool," Danny told his mom. "But the walking is getting really boring."

While they were camped by the Red Sea, Danny heard shouting. "Pharaoh's army is coming! We're trapped here! We'll all be killed! We should have stayed in Egypt!"

"Dad!" Danny yelled. "What's going to happen? How will we get across the sea?"

"It's okay, Danny," said his dad. "Moses says to wait and watch. The Lord will save us."

Danny wasn't so sure about this guy Moses. As he fell asleep that night, Danny felt the wind start to blow. In the middle of the night, his mom woke him up. People were scurrying around and some were beginning to run. Danny was surprised to see that the cloud had moved between them and Pharaoh.

"Hurry, Danny!" said his mom. "We don't want to be left behind."

"Mom, what will happen when Pharaoh catches up with us? I can't swim!" Danny reminded her.

As Danny stumbled along in the big crowd, he couldn't take his eyes off the high wall of water on each side of the sea. *What if it comes crashing down on us?* he worried. *Which is worse—drowning or being caught by Pharaoh and his army?*

By the next day, all the people had crossed the sea on dry land. Danny's feet didn't even get wet. *But what good is that?* he thought. *The Egyptian chariots will cross on dry land right behind us.*

Suddenly, there was a mighty roar as the piled-up water began to fall back into the sea.

God had stopped the Egyptians from following them. Danny and his family were safe! What a wonderful miracle! Danny began to cheer! "Yay! Yay!"

"Danny!"

Danny jumped and looked up. His dad and all the others at the Seder table were staring at him. "What are you doing? Why are you yelling at the table?"

Oh! He was at the Seder, not in Egypt. "Uh, sorry, Dad," Danny said.

His dad shook his head and went back to telling the story.

Finally, when Danny and his cousins thought they couldn't sit still another minute, Danny's mom exclaimed, "It's time to eat!"

After dinner, the children hunted for the Afikomen. Gaby was the lucky one who found it and took it to Danny's dad for a reward.

Everyone had a piece of the Afikomen for dessert. Danny wiggled in his chair. He knew he would have one more chance to ask his question.

All the cups were filled with grape juice again. This time, the special cup in the middle of the table was filled for Elijah the Prophet.

"Danny," said his dad, "please go and open the door. Maybe Elijah has come to tell us that the Messiah is on His way to bring us peace."

Danny ran to the door and carefully opened it. "There's no one here," he said. But at least, now was his big chance. "But, Dad," he said excitedly, "WHO IS THE MESSIAH?"

Danny's dad rolled his eyes and sighed. "Later, Danny," he said. "The Seder is over," he announced. "May we be allowed to celebrate it again…"

And everyone said together, "Next year in Jerusalem!"

"Let's sing some Passover songs," said Danny's dad.

Danny joined in the singing of "Who Knows One?" and "One Little Goat."

But I still have a question, he thought. *Someday I'll find the answer.*

Someday came sooner than Danny expected. On Monday, he saw Joey on the playground.

"How was your Passover?" Joey asked.

"Okay," said Danny. "Except I sure wish someone would answer my question."

"Which one?" asked Joey. "You ask lots of questions!"

"I want to know who the Messiah is!" explained Danny.

"Oh, we talked all about that at our Seder," said Joey.

"Yeah?" Danny said. "You know who He is?"

"Sure," Joey told him. "Come over after school. I think I can remember most of what my dad says about Him."

After school, Joey set some candles on the dining room table. "First, my mom lights the candles and prays. The prophet Isaiah said that the Lord will be our everlasting light. Years later in Israel, Yeshua the Messiah said that He is the light of the world."

"What? You mean this Yeshua is the Messiah?"

"Yep. And wait until you hear the rest!" Joey answered.

Next, Joey set out two cups and some grape juice. "In Exodus, Moses said our people should put the blood of a lamb on the doorpost to save their children. The grape juice makes us think of the blood on the doors in Egypt. It also makes us think of Yeshua's blood when He died on the cross to save us."

"The Messiah died?" exclaimed Danny. "Does this story have a happy ending?"

"It sure does," said Joey. "At a Seder in Jerusalem, Yeshua picked up His cup and said that this was His blood of the new covenant for forgiveness of sins. One of His special friends, John, said the blood of Yeshua, God's Son, takes away our sins. Another friend, Peter, said that we are saved by the blood of Messiah."

"Wow!" said Danny. "Is there more?"

"Well, did you have a lamb bone on your Seder plate?" Joey asked.

"Sure," said Danny. "But what does that have to do with the Messiah?"

"Remember the blood of the perfect lamb in Egypt?" asked Joey.

"Yeah."

"Okay, in Genesis, Abraham said that God would give us the lamb for the sacrifice. Yeshua, God's own Son, was the perfect Lamb of God. He took our sins away when He died for us. Now we don't have to sacrifice lambs anymore.

"When Yeshua came the first time, John the Baptizer saw Him and called Him the Lamb of God who takes away the sins of the world. One of the Jewish leaders named Paul called Yeshua Messiah our Passover Lamb."

"Wait!" said Danny. "What do you mean when He came the first time?"

"Hang on, Danny, and I'll show you," Joey answered. He handed Danny a square of matzah. "We were told to eat bread without yeast during Passover. That's matzah, right? Remember when your dad hid the Afikomen?"

"I remember," said Danny. "My cousin found it. So what?"

"At the Seder, Yeshua took the matzah," Joey told him. "He broke it and said this was His body broken for us. Look at your matzah. See the stripes on it? They remind us that Yeshua was beaten before He died. The holes remind us of the nail holes when He was on the cross. Hiding the Afikomen in a napkin shows us that Yeshua died and was buried. When someone finds the Afikomen, it shows us that Yeshua came back to life. That guy Paul said that Messiah died for our sins, was buried, and was raised up to life again."

"No kidding?" asked Danny. "If He's alive, where is He?"

"He went back to heaven," Joey told him. "But He promised that when the time is right, He will come back to Jerusalem again. This time, He'll be our king. But my dad says that we can know Messiah now if we open the door to our hearts and ask Him to live in us.

"Messiah's Hebrew name is Yeshua, but some people call Him Jesus. I know a song about the Messiah. Do you want to learn it?"

"Sure thing!" Danny said with a grin.

So Joey sang "Who Is Messiah?" two times. Then Danny sang it with him until he knew it by heart.

"That's so cool!" said Danny. "Uh-oh. It's late. I gotta get home now, but I'll see you tomorrow. Thanks a lot, Joey. Finally, I know the answer to my question!"

Who is Messiah?

by: Sandra J. Anderson

Sing Along with Danny
Who Is Messiah?

Who is Messiah?
Who can He be?
When will He be coming
To set us free?
Who is Messiah?
What's His name?
What if He already came?

Jesus is Messiah,
He's my friend.
Son of David,
Born in Bethlehem.
He came before and
He's coming back again,
Coming to Jerusalem.

Jesus loves me
This I know,
For the prophets
Tell me so.
That is why I give Him praise
YESHUA HAMASHIACH
That's His Name!

Danny walked home smiling and singing "Who Is Messiah?" As he went into his house, Danny called out, "Hey, Mom! When are we going to eat? What are we having? What's for dessert? Is Dad home? I need to ask him a question."

Parents Only

Dear parent: The following are a few of the hundreds of types and prophecies from the Tanakh (Old Testament) which were, or will be, fulfilled by Yeshua HaMashiach (Jesus the Messiah). They are listed for background information in case you have a Danny in your family.

Prophecy	*Fulfillment*
Virgin Birth (Isaiah 7:14)	Matthew 1:18–23; Luke 1:26–31
Born in Bethlehem (Micah 5:2)	Matthew 2:1; Luke 2:4–7
Tribe of Judah (Genesis 49:10)	Luke 3:33; Hebrews 7:14
Son of David (Isaiah 9:6–7; Psalm 110:1)	Luke 1:32–33; Matthew 22:41–46
Called Emmanuel (Isaiah 7:14)	Matthew 1:20–23
The Messiah (Isaiah 53:1–12; Daniel 9:24–26)	Luke 2:8–15, 25–32; Matthew 16:15–17
Messiah Forgives Sins (Isaiah 53:4–12, 43:25)	Acts 5:31; 1 Peter 1:18–19
Entry to Jerusalem (Zechariah 9:9)	Matthew 21:1–9; Luke 19:28–38
Crucified with Criminals (Isaiah 53:12)	Matthew 27:38; Mark 15:27–28
Messiah Pierced (Psalm 22:16; Zechariah 12:10)	Luke 24:37–40; Revelation 1:7
Messiah Buried with Rich (Isaiah 53:9)	Matthew 27:57–60
Messiah Resurrected (Psalm 16:10, 49:15)	Acts 2:32; Luke 24:46
Messiah Ascends to Heaven (Psalm 68:18)	Mark 16:19; Luke 24:51

Messiah's Return (Zechariah 14:3–4)	Acts 1:10–11; Revelation 1:7
God the Creator (Isaiah 40:28, 42:5, 45:18)	Colossians 1:15–17; John 1:1–3
The First and Last (Isaiah 44:6, 48:12)	Revelation 1:17–18, 21:6–7, 22:13
Bread from Heaven (Exodus 16:4; Psalm 105:40)	John 6:33, 35, 48–51
Living Water (Jeremiah 2:13, 17:13; Isaiah 12:3)	John 4:9–14; Revelation 22:17
King (Isaiah 43:15; Jeremiah 10:10, 23:5–6)	Luke 19:37–38; Revelation 19:16
Redeemer (Job 19:25; Psalm 19:14; Jeremiah 50:34)	Luke 1:68; Galatians 4:4–7
Lamb (Genesis 22:7–8; Exodus 12:5; Isaiah 53:7)	John 1:36; Revelation 14 and 21
Light (Psalm 27:1; Isaiah 9:2, 60:19–20; Micah 7:8)	John 1:6–9, 8:12, 9:5; Revelation 21:23
Shepherd (Psalm 23, 79:13, 80:1; Isaiah 40:11)	John 10:11; Hebrews 13:20; 1 Peter 2:25
Shema (Deuteronomy 6:4–5)	Mark 12:28–30; Matthew 22:34–38
Covenant (Jeremiah 31:31–33)	Hebrews 8:6–10:18

About the Author

Sandy Anderson was a fortunate child whose parents loved to read. Every two weeks, they took her to the public library where they all checked out books. Later, she held a children's story hour in the same library. She became an elementary school teacher in Arizona; after raising her two sons in California, she worked with special education high school students. Now she lives again in Arizona where she is still reading—and writing.

CPSIA information can be obtained
at www.ICGtesting.com
Printed in the USA
LVHW071111210322
713978LV00016B/798